# CAST ALL CHANGE

Exclusive Distributors:
**Music Sales Limited**
8/9 Frith Street, London W1V 5TZ, England.
**Music Sales Pty Limited**
120 Rothschild Avenue, Rosebery, NSW 2018, Australia.

Order No. AM937740
ISBN 0-7119-5784-3

This book © Copyright 1996 by Wise Publications.

Visit the Music Sales' Internet Music Shop at
http://www.musicsales.co.uk

Music arranged by Roger Day.
Music processed by MSS Studios.

**Your Guarantee of Quality:**
As publishers, we strive to produce every book to the highest commercial standards.
The music has been freshly engraved and, whilst endeavouring to retain the original
running order of the recorded album, the book has been carefully designed to minimise
awkward page turns and to make playing from it a real pleasure.

Particular care has been given to specifying acid-free, neutral-sized paper made from pulps
which have not been elemental chlorine bleached. This pulp is from farmed sustainable forests
and was produced with special regard for the environment. Throughout, the printing and binding
have been planned to ensure a sturdy, attractive publication which should give years of enjoyment.
If your copy fails to meet our high standards, please inform us and we will gladly replace it.

Music Sales' complete catalogue describes thousands of titles and is available
in full colour sections by subject, direct from Music Sales Limited.
Please state your areas of interest and send a cheque/postal order for £1.50 for postage to:
Music Sales Limited, Newmarket Road, Bury St. Edmunds, Suffolk IP33 3YB.

This publication is not authorised for sale in
the United States of America and/or Canada.

**Wise Publications**
London / New York / Paris / Sydney / Copenhagen / Madrid

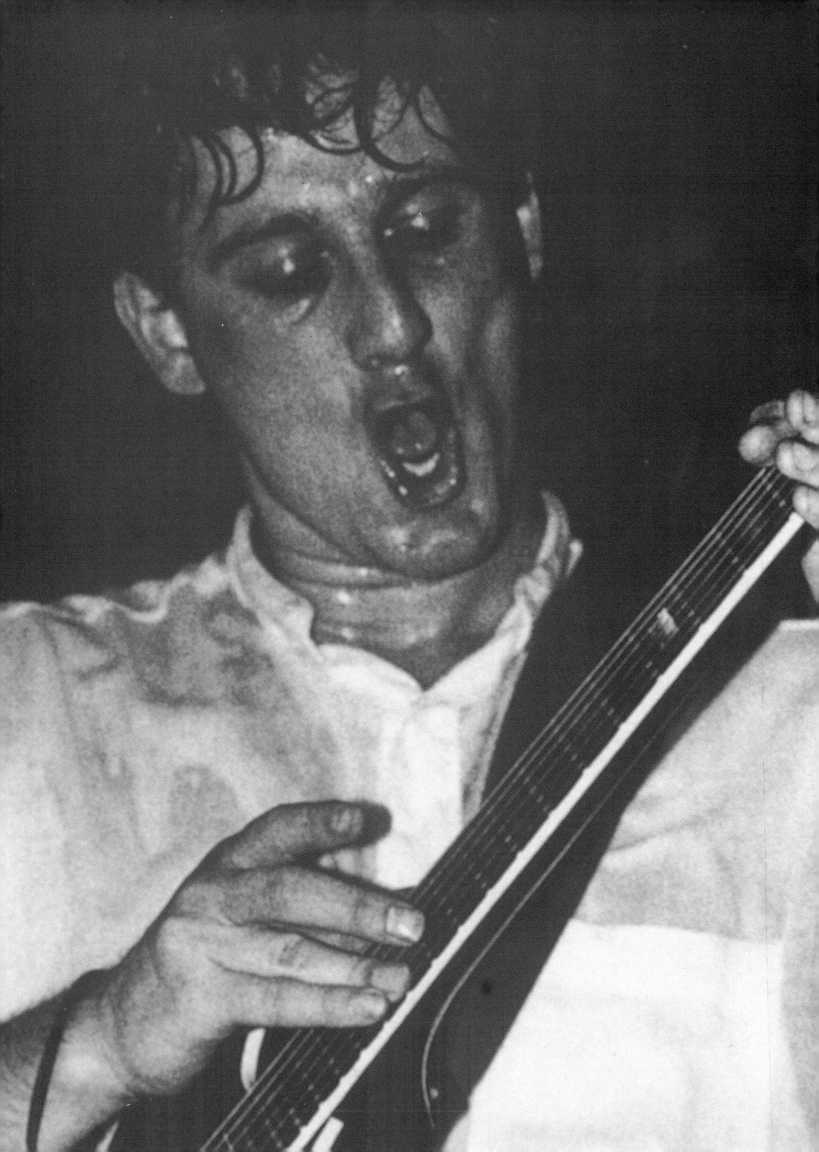

## ALRIGHT

I guess I'm alright, guess I'm alright.
I guess I'm doing fine, guess I'm doing fine.
Do you think I'd miss you, do you think I'd care?
Do you think I'd lay down and die?

You never even tried,
You never even tried.

Now it's about time, it's the right time,
If you willed your mind, if you willed your mind.
So fly on swift now on your journey home
And you fled the nest now and you have flown.

Ain't nothing you don't know,
Ain't nothing you don't know.

Look out to sea and tell me what we came here for.
Is it what they say or is there more than we can know,
And if so, which way am I to go,
Which way am I to go?

I guess I'm alright, I guess I'm alright.
I guess I'm doing fine, I guess I'm doing fine.
Can't see no reasons for not pushing through
So make like the wind that's blowing you.

Ain't nothing you can do,
Ain't nothing you can do.

## SANDSTORM

I've got a sandstorm blowing in my head,
I'm seein' many colours but the only one that's coming through is red,
It's stopping me dead, tryin' to make some tracks but my feet they're feeling like lead,
Stop being bled, stop being bled oh.

Say oh my things aren't the same,
Anyone could see that if I stayed much longer I'd be tamed,
We stopped playing games, I'm not pointing fingers, but I'm not taking all the blame,
Playin' all your games taking all your blame. Oh.

I said oh no, I don't even care,
I guess I'll be seein' you I guess I'll be leaving you today,
We're just not a pair,
I know you've been trying but I just can't bear to tell a lie
Stop tellin' me all your lies
Stop tellin' me all your lies
Lies.

Let me take you by the hand, try to understand,
Walk me to a land, try to understand,
I ain't nothing but a man.

I've got a sandstorm blowin' in my head,
I'm seein' many colours but the only one that's coming through is red,
You know how we feel
We can't go on pretending, and we've just got to fix the deal,
Gotta make it real, gotta make it real. Oh.

## PROMISED LAND

You say you caught a glimpse
Of a man with reverence,
And if you could ever meet,
Would you please report to me.
Tell me what did he say
To change your day,
And keep the fear at bay.
If you did, you better learn to pray.

I'm sure I heard them say
There'll come a time when all must pay
And every penny that you spend
You're gonna pay back in the end.
Tell me, was it worth the cost
If all is lost
And the world is robbed.
The only sound is the echo of your sob.

And so the fire burned
And in the final days the world refused to turn,
And all the oceans turned to sand.
Ain't nothing left of your promised land.
Got to learn to change our ways
If you want to live and breathe another day.
But what it is you just can't believe,
We're coming in out of the dark,
We're gonna reach high for the stars,
We're gonna take back what is ours.

But with a kiss you will betray
And all you give you take away.
And in our finest hour
We recognised the taste is sour.
Tell me, was it worth the cost
If all is lost
And the world is robbed.
The only sound is the echo of your sob.

And so the fire burned
And in the final days the world refused to turn,
And all the oceans turned to sand.
Ain't nothing left of your promised land.
Got to learn to change our ways
If you want to live and breathe another day.
But what it is you just can't believe,
We're coming in out of the cold,
We're gonna buy before we get sold,
We're gonna make new what is old.

We're coming in out of the dark,
We're gonna reach high for the stars,
We're gonna take back what is ours.

We're coming in out of the cold,
We're gonna buy before we get sold,
We're gonna make new what is old.
And free our soul.

## MANKIND

When you start to find, start to see the signs,
Read between the lines, then you start to learn,
Wheels start to turn, like fire burns.

I tried to show you but you could not see me.
I tried to tell you but you could not hear me, no,
So I just let go.

Then you realise that all can't be defined.
The questions in your mind, then you open wide.
And see what's yet to come.
Now it's only just begun.

I tried to signal but you do not receive me.
I tried the truth, but you will not believe me, no,
So I just let go.

'Cause I can see the things I need to see, come alive with energy,
And I'm a big believer in mankind,
Watch the world revolving through my eyes,
Watch the world evolving in my mind.

When you start to learn, wheels start to turn, fire burns.
Then you open wide and see what's yet to come.
Now it's only just begun.

I tried to touch but I could not reach you.
You hear the prayer, but will you be preached to, no.

Watch the world revolving through my eyes,
See the world evolving in my mind,
And the world turns round and round,
To the music and the sound.
Hear the world responding to our cry.

## TELL IT LIKE IT IS

Oh, here it comes again, I feel the heat again.
Blaze to the very end, rise like the sun again.

I'm on my feet but I can't seem to stand,
Got control but I ain't got command,
The things I need slip through my hand.

So I tell it like it is, always hit or miss,
Tell me to my face, like it really is.
But then you make it plain to see,
Straight from you to me.

Oh, here it comes again, I feel the need again.
To burn like a flame again, blow like a hurricane.

And when I look I just don't recognise,
It's all off course and bound to collide.
The truth I hear is a truth full of lies.

I'm on my feet but I can't seem to stand,
Got control but I ain't got command,
The things I need slip through my hand.

So I tell it like it is, always hit or miss,
Tell me to my face, like it really is.
But then you make it plain to see,
Straight from you to me.

'Cause it gets better each time, better each time I'm told.
It gets better each time, better.
It gets better, better.
It gets better.

## FOUR WALLS

These four walls are destined to stay.
They say I'm guilty and the guilty must pay.
But all I'm askin' is to have a' my say,
Do you think I'll ever get out?

Will I ever get out of here,
Will I ever push down my fear,
Will I ever see through my tears,
Will I ever get out of here tonight.

The sands of time them falling right through my hand.
Can't make no sense and I can't make no plan.
All I'm askin' is to lend me your hand,
Come on and help me get out.

Will I ever get out of here,
Will I ever push down my fear,
Will I ever see through my tears,
Will I ever get out of here tonight.

Will I ever get out of here,
Will I ever push down my fear,
Will I ever see through my tears,
Will I ever get out of here tonight.

So at last I'm feeling the pain
Can't take the weight and I can't take the strain.
Can't see no future and I can't see no gain
Looks like we never get out.

Will I ever get out of here,
Will I ever push down my fear,
Will I ever see through my tears,
Will I ever get out of here.
Well I guess I'll never know,
I guess I'll never know, I guess I'll never know,
Am I free, am I free to go,
Am I free, am I free to go?

Well I guess I'll never know,
I guess I'll never know, I guess I'll never know,
Are we free, are we free to go?
I don't know.

## FINETIME

So what's it all about, do you really want to know?
Do you want to give or do you just want to take it all and go?
'Cause you've got to let it out if you want to let it in.
Got to get a little bit of loving in and make it all begin.

You've got to find time to pick the right time to make a change.
'Cause it's a fine time to pick the right time to make a change.

So when you gonna learn that it takes all sorts.
Don't you think life would be a little drab if we had the same thoughts.
'Cause you've taken all the good and you leave me with the bad.
And if you don't make a change pretty soon there won't be nothing coming back.

You've got to find time to pick the right time to make a change.
'Cause it's a fine time to pick the right time to make a change.

I do believe you read the verse,
I do believe you wrote the words.
I just need to let you out to let you in again,
I just need to feel your love again and again.

You've got to find time to pick the right time to make a change.
'Cause it's a fine time to pick the right time to make a change.

So what's it all about, do you really want to know?
Do you want to give or do you just want to take it all and go?
'Cause you've got to let it out if you want to let it in.
Got to get a little bit of loving in and make it all begin.

You've got to find time to pick the right time to make a change.
'Cause it's a fine time to pick the right time to make a change.

I do believe you read the verse,
I do believe you wrote the words.
I just need to let you out to let you in again,
I just need to feel your love again and again,
And again, and again.


## BACK OF MY MIND

They say they'll take it away to reassure them, that the future is theirs.
I hear the words that they say but don't believe them,
We take the control, the hour's taking its toll.

From the back of my mind, I can hear you.
From the corner of my eye, I still see you.
We all believe in you.

Everything that you need is right beside you, but you turn it away.
You've got an instinct inside that's there to guide you,
When you make your own way, we chase the future today.

From the back of my mind, I can hear you.
From the corner of my eye, I still see you.
We all believe in you.

From the back of my mind, I can hear you.
From the corner of my eye, I still see you.
We all believe in you.

From the back of my mind, from the back of my mind,
From the back of my mind, from the back of my mind.

Everything that you see stands right before you if you open your eyes.
Understand your beliefs and we'll expect you to know where it's at,
Man it's as simple as that.

From the back of my mind, I can hear you.
From the corner of my eye, I still see you.
We all believe in you.

You take the control, the hour's taking it's toll.
Don't throw it away, you take the future today,
You take the future away, we have the future today.


## WALKAWAY

If you've heard all they've got to say,
You looked but turned away, just walk away, walk away.
If you've said all you've got to say,
Now your words just slip away, just walk away, walk away, walk away.
That's what they say, what they say, what they say.
You've gotta walk away.

If you've played all the games they play,
You played them yesterday, just walk away, walk away.
If you've been where they wanna go
Seen all they've got to show, just walk away, walk away, walk away.
That's what they say, what they say, what they say,
Gotta walk away.

Now you must believe me, you never lose your dream.
So now you must believe me, we never lose our dreams.

If you've proved all there is to prove,
Got nothing left to lose, just walk away, walk away.
If you've done all there is to do
Ain't nothing left for you, just walk away, walk away, walk away.
That's what they say, what they say, what they say,
Walk away, walk away, walk away.
That's what they say, what they say, what they say.
Gotta walk away today.


## REFLECTIONS

Well I can see my reflection, reflecting in you
And I can feel the connection, connecting the two.

It's dream reality trying to break free and wake me,
Dream reality, trying to break free from this world, from the world.

Well I can feel your reactions, reacting with mine.
And now I sense things are happening, and they're happening on time.

It's dream reality trying to break free and wake me,
Dream reality, trying to break free from this world, from the world.

Dream reality trying to break free and wake me,
Dream reality, trying to break free from this world.
Free from this world, set me free from this world,
Free from the world.

Well I can feel your direction, directing me on line.
And I believe you're responding, responding to your mind.

It's dream reality trying to break free and wake me,
Dream reality, trying to break free from this world, free from the world.
Free from this world, from the world.


## HISTORY

I was born to live and I live to give,
I'm the love that you feel, the life that lives real in all you.
I was born to die and I live to cry,
And I'm your tormented soul, blackness that holds to all you.

So think of me as history,
And I will leave to you all that I do.

Well I've walked this earth since woman gave birth.
I'm a seed that's sown, the harvest is grown in all you.
But I've laid to waste my future in haste,
I'm the crops that have failed, the burden that's nailed to all you.

So think of me as history,
And I will leave to you all that I do.

So think of me as history,
And I will leave to you all that I do.
All love is holy, all love is holy,
All love is holy, our love is holy.

I'm the cloud that bursts, I rain down for your thirst.
I'm the thunder you hear, the lightning that spears your night.
I'm the shadow that is cast, I project all your past.
I'm the children you burn, the cross that is turned by all you.

So think of me as history,
And I will leave to you all that I do.
All that you do, all that you do.
All that you do, all that you do.


## TWO OF A KIND

Can you help me, help me if you can,
For I'm in need of a helping hand, or some understanding.
I feel I'm sinking, sinking with the boat,
I'm trying to stay afloat, someone throw me some hope.

Can you help me to set my course,
I'm aiming for better shores.
And when I get there, I hope to find
A key to fit the lock and open up my mind.

Please throw me a line, I'm lost here in time,
I'm locked in my mind, please hold back the tide.

Feel I'm drifting, drifting with the tide.
Let the ocean be my guide, waves I shall ride.
And then I'm sinking. Sinking in the depth
And I'm trying to catch my breath, but no breath is left.

Can you help me to set my course,
I'm aiming for better shores.
And when I get there, I hope to find
A key to fit the lock and open up my mind.

Please throw me a line, I'm lost here in time,
I'm locked in my mind, please hold back the tide.

Life pushes hard when you're down
And we're all lost until we're found, until we're found, until we're found.

Please throw me a line, I'm lost here in time,
I'm locked in my mind, please hold back the tide.

And from nowhere someone shines a light
And sends to me some sight and gives back some life.
And she gave all that she can give.
She gives me the will to live, love's eternal gift.

So at last we meet again, together now until the end.
We are as one and all is saved, and now it's time to turn, turn the final page.

Together we find a place here in time.
Together in mind, all ways to shine.

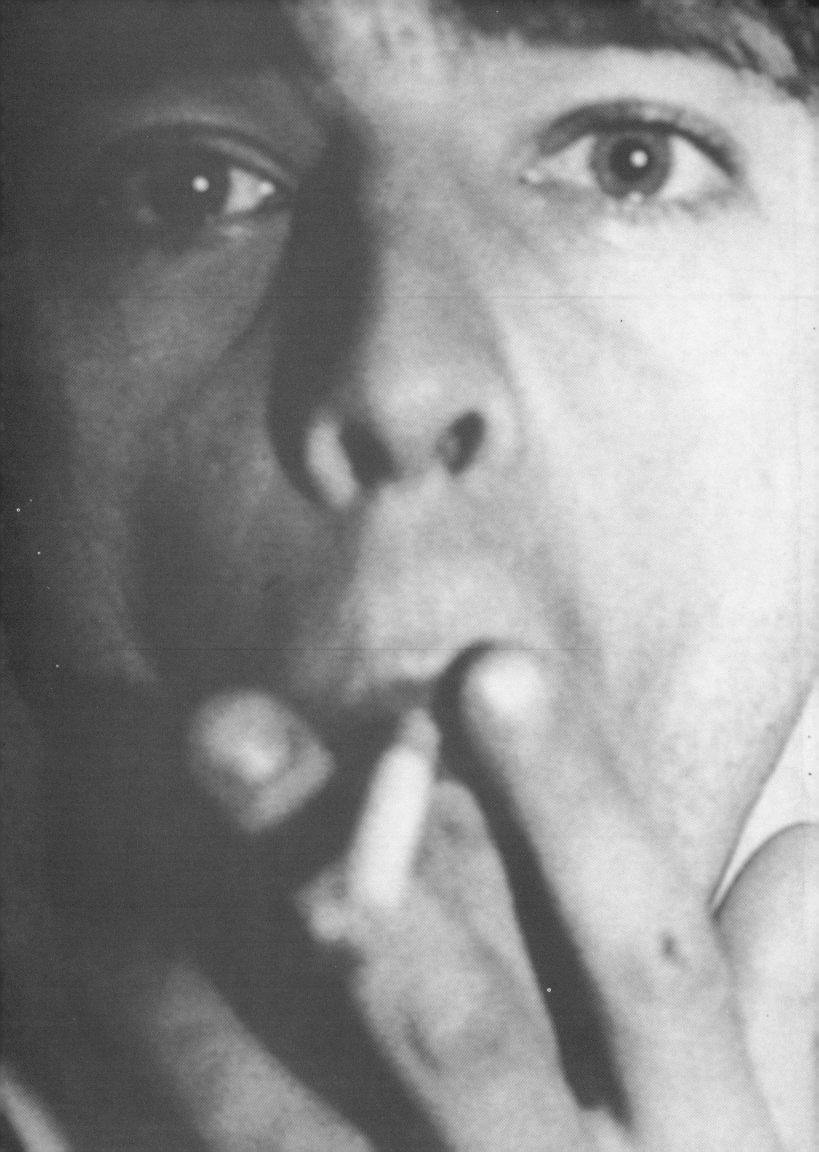

# ALRIGHT

Words & Music by John Power

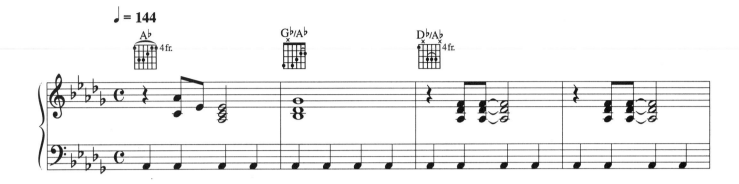

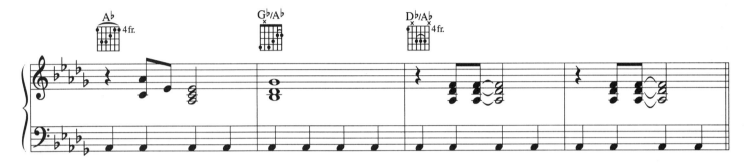

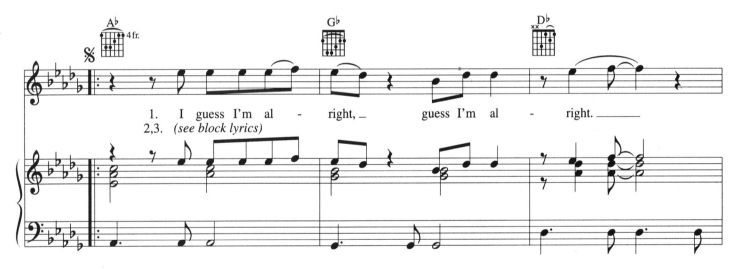

1. I guess I'm al - right, _ guess I'm al - right. _____
2,3. *(see block lyrics)*

I guess I'm do - ing fine, _ guess I'm do - ing

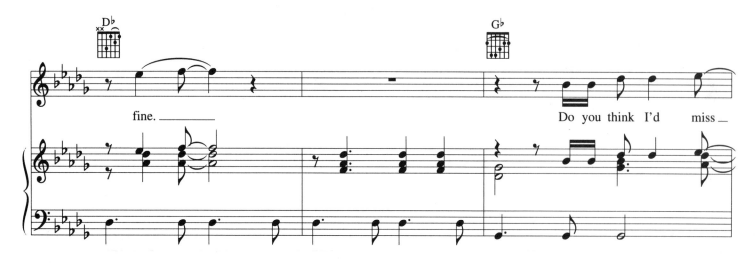

fine. _____

Do you think I'd miss _

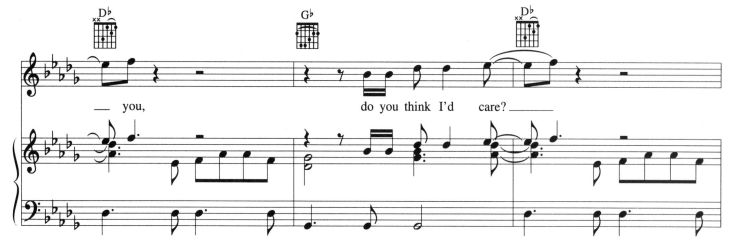

_ you,

do you think I'd care? _____

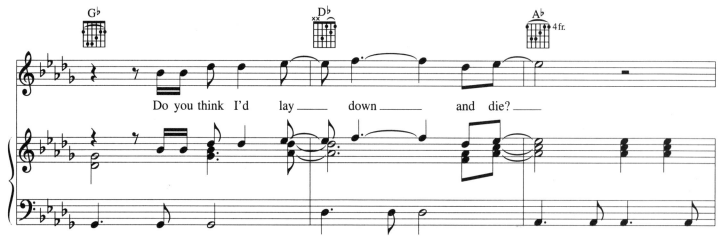

Do you think I'd lay ___ down ___ and die? _____

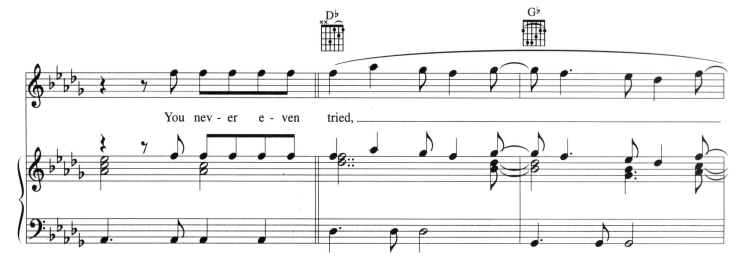

You nev-er e-ven tried, _____

you nev - er e - ven tried.

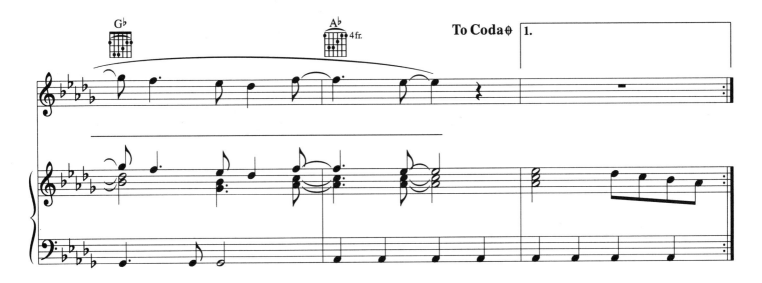

To Coda ⊕ 1.

2.

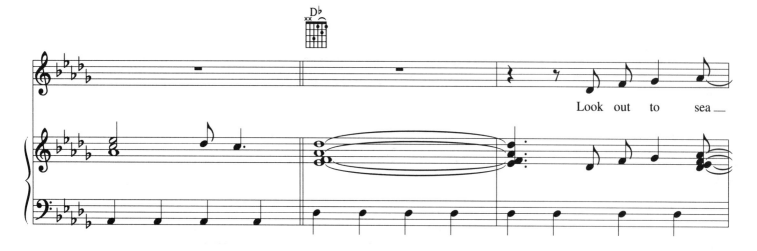

Look out to sea ___

and tell me what ___ we came ___ here for. ___

Is it what they say ___

or is ___ there more than we can know ___ and if so, ___

which way am I to go, _____

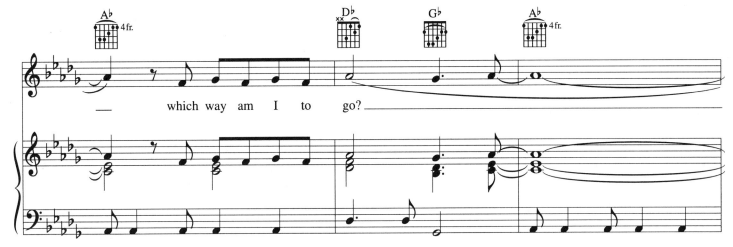

which way am I to go? _____

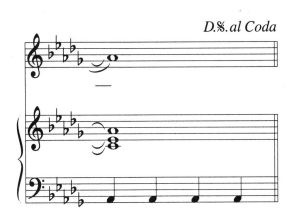

*D.%.al Coda*

**Ⓞ Coda**

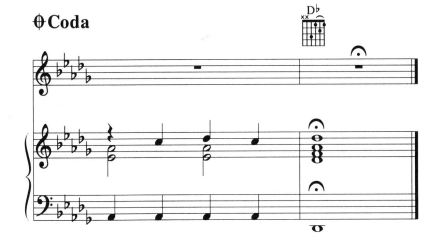

*Verse 2:*
Now it's about time, it's the right time.
If you willed your mind, if you willed your mind.
So fly on swift now on your journey home
And you fled the nest now and you have flown.

Ain't nothing you don't know
Ain't nothing you don't know

*Verse 3:*
I guess I'm alright, I guess I'm alright
I guess I'm doing fine, I guess I'm doing fine
Can't see no reasons for not pushing through
So make like the wind that's blowing you.

Ain't nothing you can do
Ain't nothing you can do

# PROMISED LAND

Words & Music by John Power

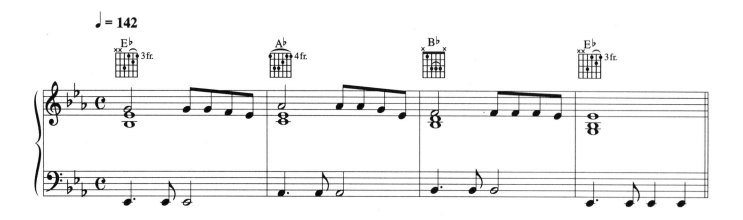

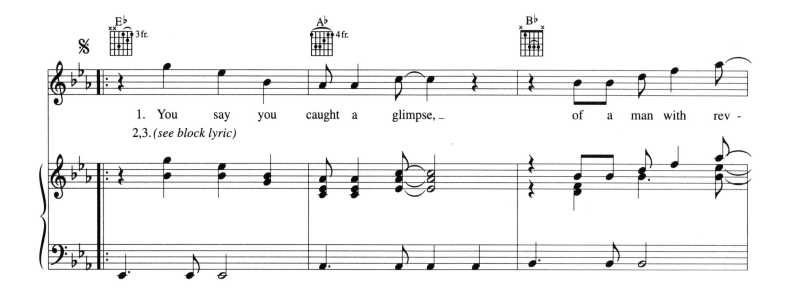

1. You say you caught a glimpse, ___ of a man with rev -
2,3. *(see block lyric)*

- er - ence, ___ and if ___ you could ev - er meet, ___

would you please re - port \_\_\_\_ to me. \_\_\_\_ Tell me what did he say \_\_\_\_

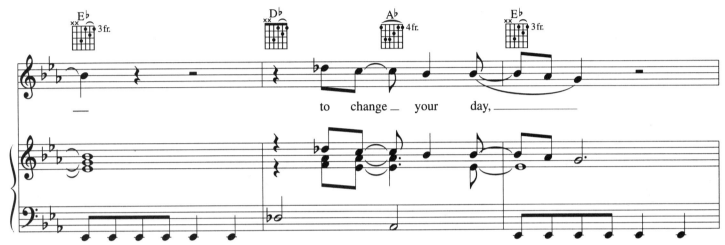

\_\_\_\_ to change \_\_\_\_ your day, _____

and keep the fear at bay. \_\_\_\_ If you did, you bet -

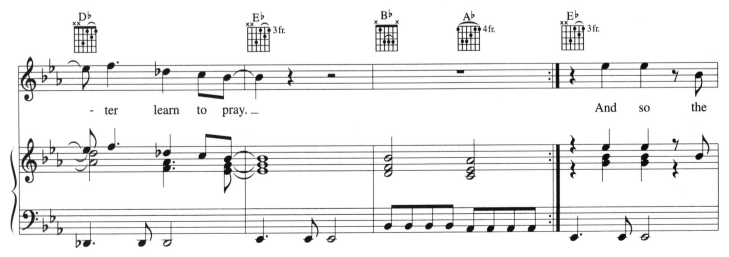

- ter learn to pray. \_\_\_\_ And so the

fi - re burned \_\_ and in the fi - nal days the world \_\_ re - fused to

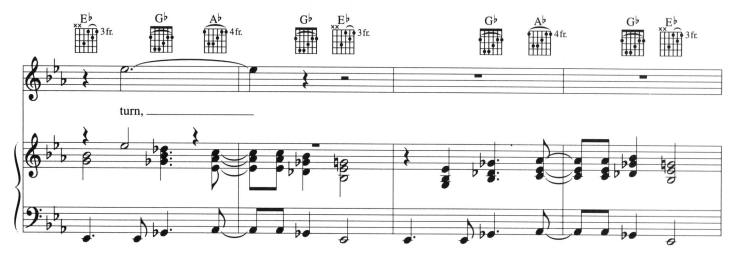

turn, _____

and all the o - ceans turned to sand. \_\_ Ain't no - thing left of our

pro - mised land. _____ Got to learn to change our ways \_\_

if you want to live and breathe __ an - oth - er day. ____

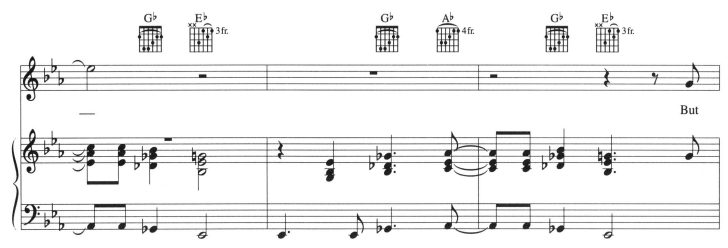

__ But

**To Coda**

what it is __ you just can't be - lieve, __ we're com - ing in out of the dark, __

__ we're gon - na reach high for the stars, ____ we're gon - na

take    back what is ours. ___

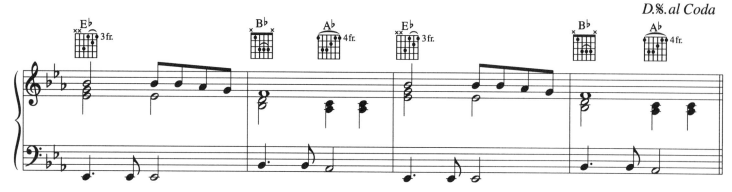

*D.%.al Coda*

**⊕ Coda**

1,3. in    out of the cold, ___    we're gon-na  buy    be-fore we get sold, __
2. in    out of the dark, ___    we're gon-na  reach    high for the stars, __

___  we're gon-na  make    new what is old. ___
___  we're gon-na  take    back what is ours. ___

We're com-ing
We're com-ing

And free our soul. __

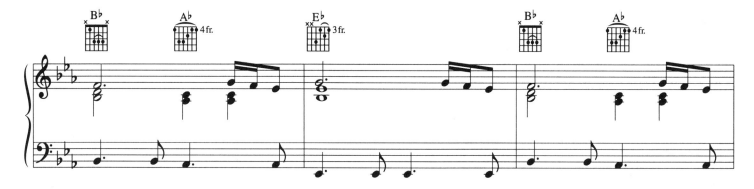

**rall.**

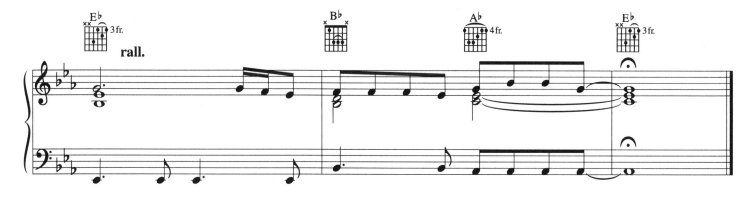

*Verse 2:*
I'm sure I heard them say
There'll come a time when all must pay
And every penny that you spend
You're gonna pay back in the end.
Tell me, was it worth the cost
If all is lost
And the world is robbed
The only sound is the echo of your sob.

*Verse 3:*
But with a kiss you will betray
And all you give you take away
And in our finest hour
We recognised the taste is sour
Tell me, was it worth the cost
If all is lost
And the world is robbed
The only sound is the echo of your sob.

# SANDSTORM

Words & Music by John Power

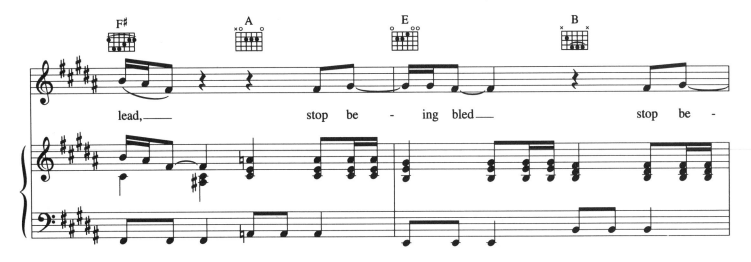

lead,_____ stop be - ing bled_____ stop be -

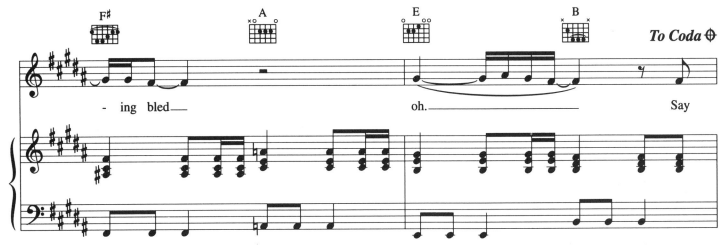

- ing bled_____ oh._____ Say

oh my things aren't the same, a - ny - one could see that if I stayed much long - er I'd be

*(2° instrumental)*

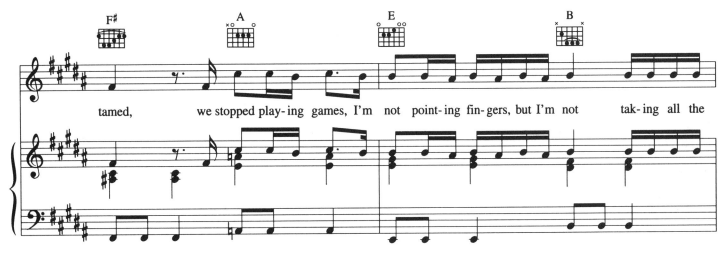

tamed, we stopped play - ing games, I'm not point - ing fin - gers, but I'm not tak - ing all the

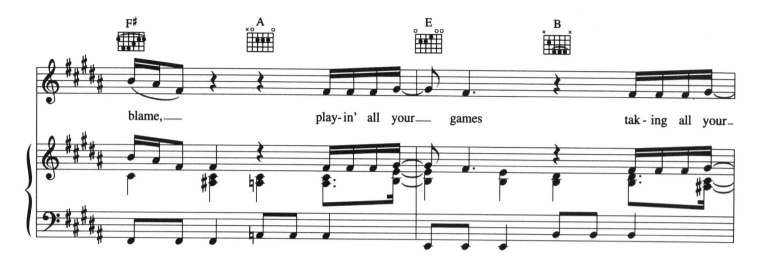

blame, \_\_\_\_ play-in' all your\_\_\_ games tak - ing all your\_

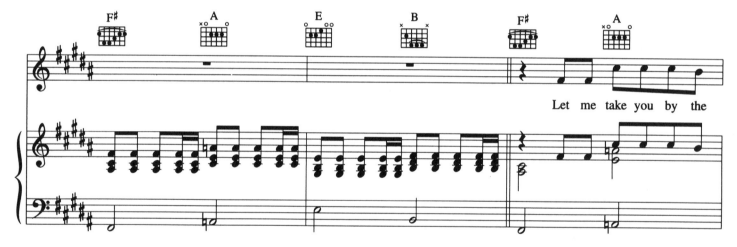

\_\_\_ blame. Oh._____ 2. I said

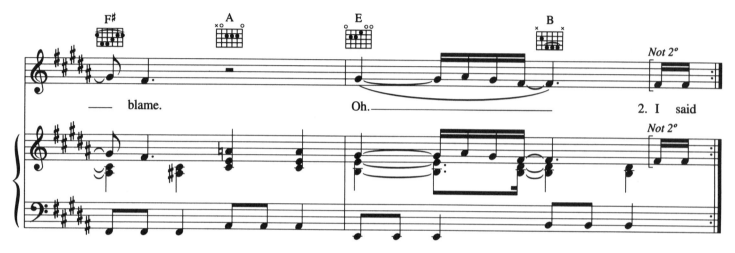

Let me take you by the

hand, try to un - der - stand, walk me to a land, try to un - der -

*Verse 2:*

I said oh no, I don't even care,
I guess I'll be seein' you I guess I'll be leaving you today,
We're just not a pair,
I know you've been trying but I just can't bear to tell a lie
Stop tellin' me all your lies
Stop tellin' me all your lies
Lies.

*Instrumental 8 bars*

*Verse 3:*

I've got a sandstorm blowin' in my head,
I'm seein' many colours but the only one that's coming through is red,
You know how we feel
We can't go on pretending, and we've just got to fix the deal,
Gotta make it real
Gotta make it real
Oh.

# MANKIND

Words & Music by John Power

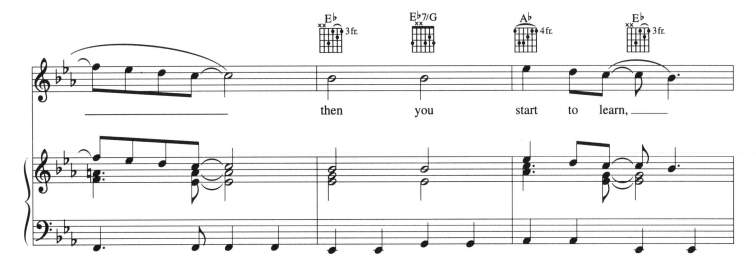

then you start to learn,

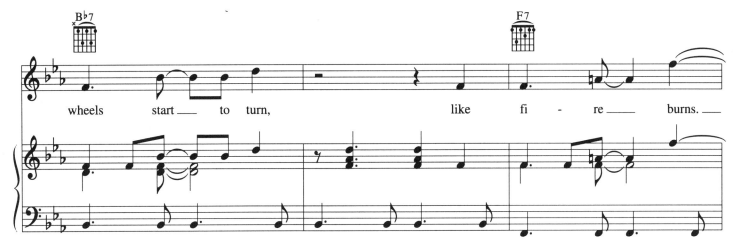

wheels start to turn, like fi-re burns.

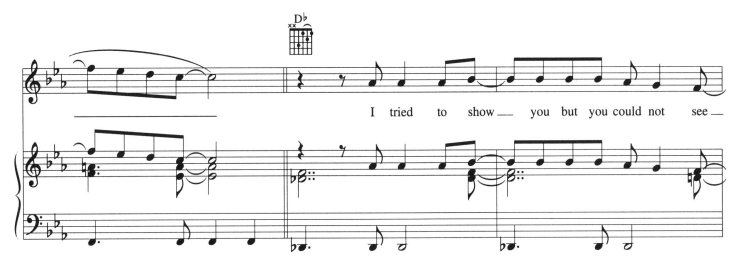

I tried to show you but you could not see

me. I tried to tell

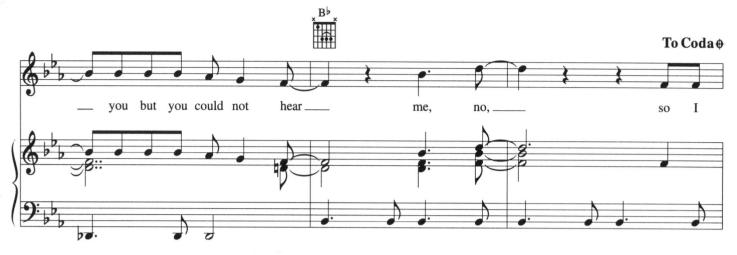

you but you could not hear ___ me, no, ___ so I

just let ___ go. ___ ___ 'Cause I can

see the things I need ___ to see, come a- live with en -

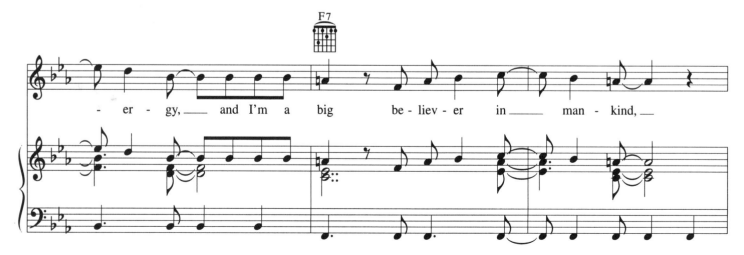

- er - gy, ___ and I'm a big be - liev - er in ___ man - kind, ___

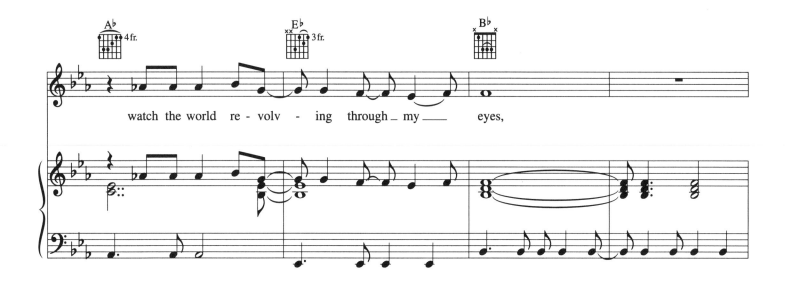

watch the world re - volv - ing through — my — eyes,

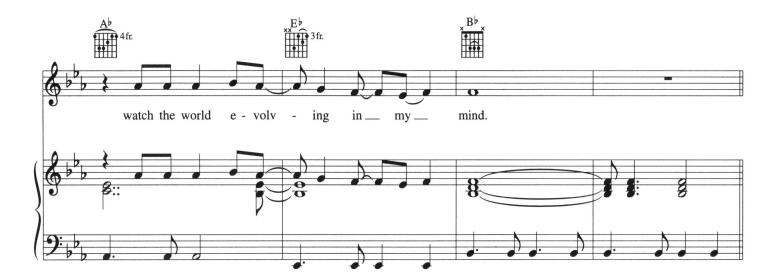

watch the world e - volv - ing in — my — mind.

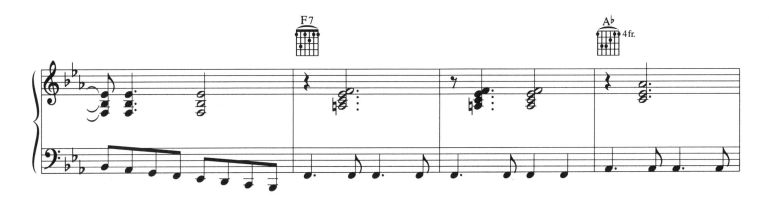

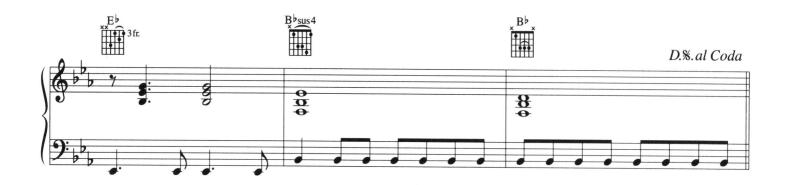

*D.%.al Coda*

⊕ **Coda**

watch the world re - volv - ing through my _____ eyes,
see the world e - volv - ing in _____ my _____ mind,

and the world turns round _____ and round, _____

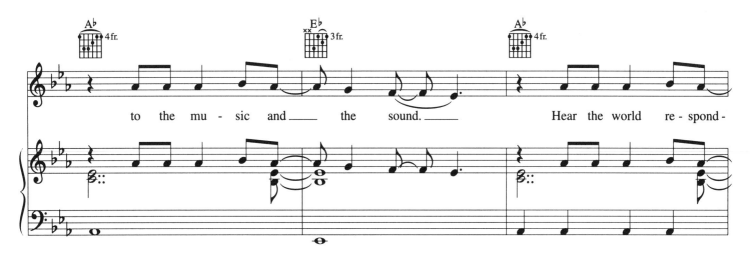

to the mu - sic and ___ the sound. ___ Hear the world re - spond -

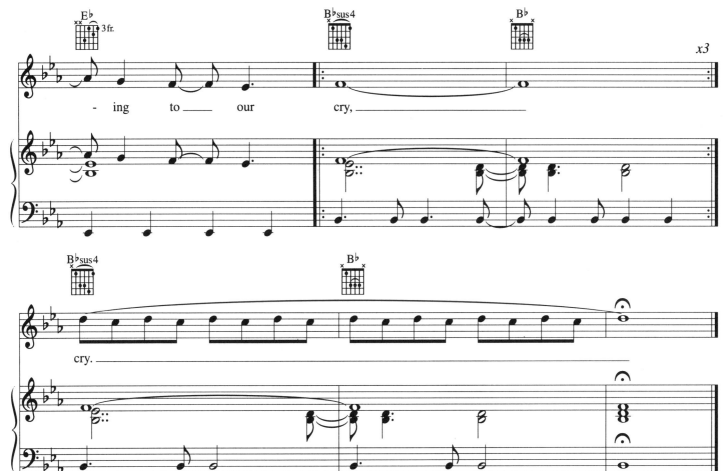

- ing to ___ our cry, ___

cry. ___

*Verse 2:*
Then you realise
That all can't be defined
The questions in your mind.
Then you open wide
And see what's yet to come
Now it's only just begun.

I tried to signal
But you do not receive me.
I tried the truth
But you will not believe me, no
So I just let go.

*Verse 3:*
When you start to learn
Wheels start to turn
Fire burns.
Then you open wide
And see what's yet to come
Now it's only just begun.

I tried to touch
But I could not reach you.
You hear the prayer
But will you be preached to, no.

# TELL IT LIKE IT IS

Words & Music by John Power

Blaze to the ve - ry end,

Rise like the sun a- gain.

*(3° vocal)*

1,3. I'm on my feet but I can't seem to stand, got con - trol but I

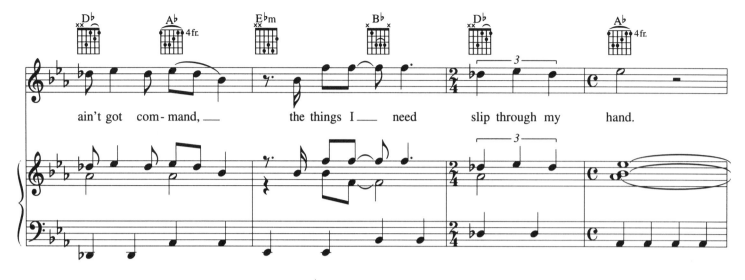

ain't got com - mand, \_\_\_ the things I \_\_\_ need slip through my hand.

So I \_\_\_ tell it like \_\_\_ it is,

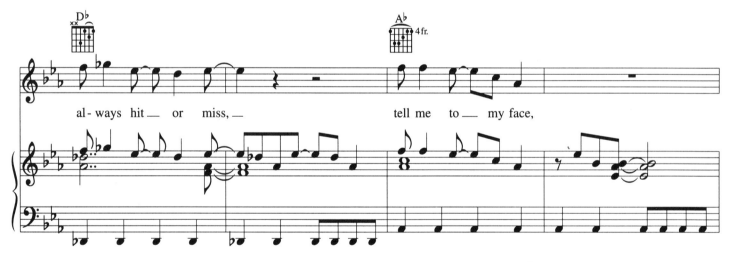

al - ways hit \_\_ or miss, \_\_\_ tell me to \_\_ my face,

like it real - ly is. But then you make it plain \_\_ to see, \_\_\_

*Verse 2:*
Oh, here it comes again
I feel the need again
To burn like a flame again
Blow like a hurricane.

And when I look I just don't recognise
It's all off course and bound to collide
The truth I hear is a truth full of lies

# FOUR WALLS

Words & Music by John Power

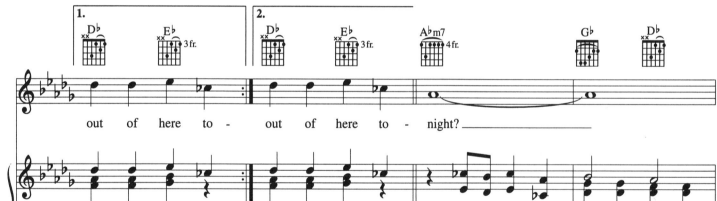

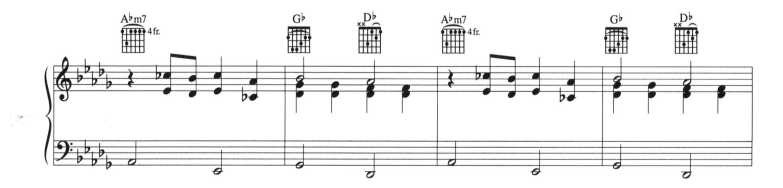

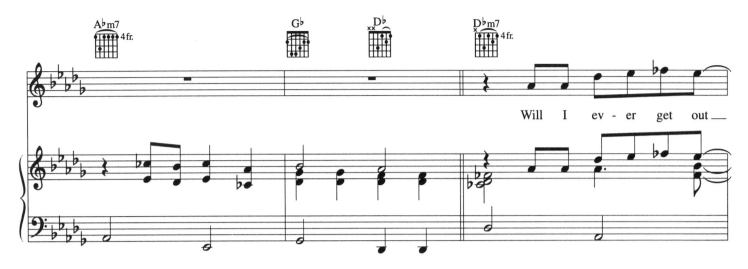

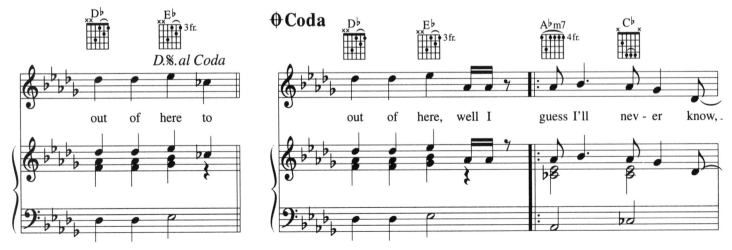

I guess I'll nev-er know, ___ I

guess I'll nev-er know. ___ Am I free, am I free to go, ___

{ am I / are we } free, { am I / are we } free to go? ___ Well I

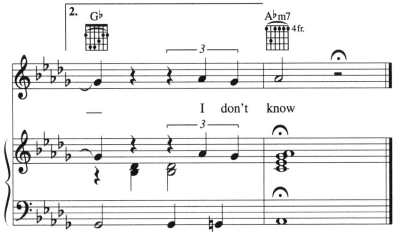

I don't know

*Verse 2:*
The sands of time them falling right through my hand
Can't make no sense and I can't make no plan
All I'm askin' is to lend me your hand
Come on and help me get out.

*Verse 3:*
So at last I'm feeling the pain
Can't take the weight and I can't take the strain
Can't see no future and I can't see no gain
Looks like we never get out.

37

# FINETIME

Words & Music by John Power

So what's it all a-bout, do you real-ly want to know?

(1,4.) what's it all a-bout, do you real-ly want to know?
2. (see block lyric)

Do you want to give or do you just want to take it all and go? 'Cause you've

got to let it out                    if you want to let it in,

got to get a lit-tle bit of lov-ing in        and make it all be-gin        *(3° vocal)* (1,2,3,4.) You've got to

find time    to pick the right time    to make a change.        'Cause it's a —

**1, 3.**

— fine time    to pick the right time    to make a change.        2. So

make a change.                                          I  do  be - lieve you read  the  verse,

—                                              I  do  be - lieve you wrote the words.

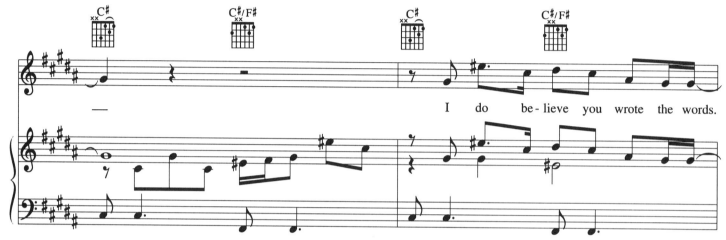

—                                  I  just  need  to  let  you  out ___  to

let  you  in ___  a - gain, ___            I  just  need  to  feel  your love ___  a - gain ___

D.%. al Coda

and a - gain.

**Coda**

and a - gain ___ and a - gain _

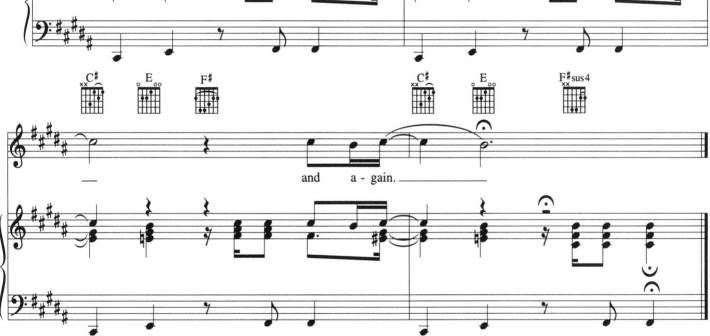

and a - gain. ___

*Verse 2:*
So when you gonna learn
That it takes all sorts
Don't you think life would be a little drab
If we had the same thoughts.
'Cause you've taken all the good
And you leave me with the bad
And if you don't make a change pretty soon
There won't be nothing coming back.

# BACK OF MY MIND

Words & Music by John Power

1. They say they'll take it a-way — to re-as-sure them, —
2,4. (see block lyric)

that the fu-ture is theirs. — I hear the words that they say, —

— but don't be-lieve them, — we take the con-trol, —

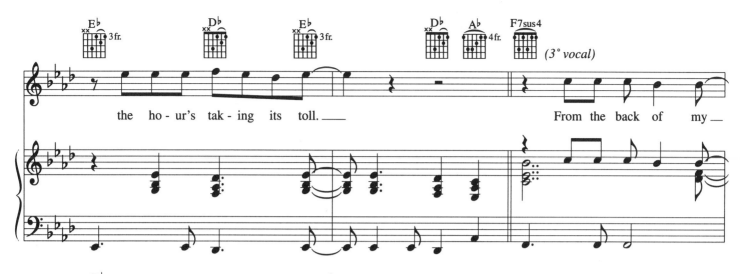

the ho - ur's tak - ing its toll. _____ From the back of my _____

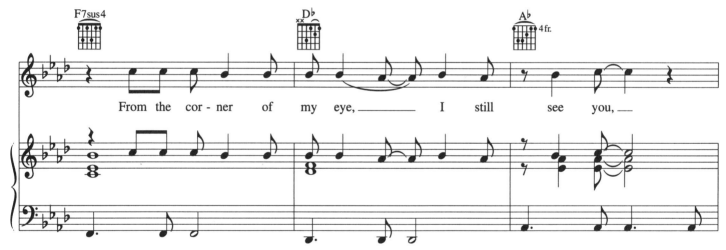

_____ mind, _____ I can hear you. _____

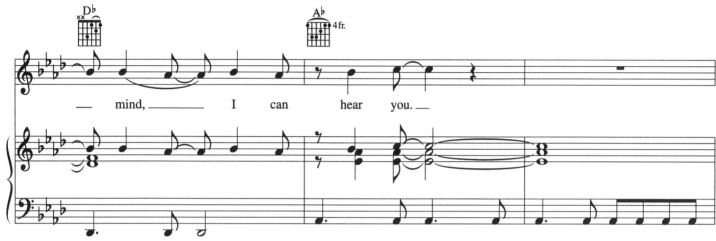

From the cor - ner of my eye, _____ I still see you, _____

we all be - lieve in you. _____

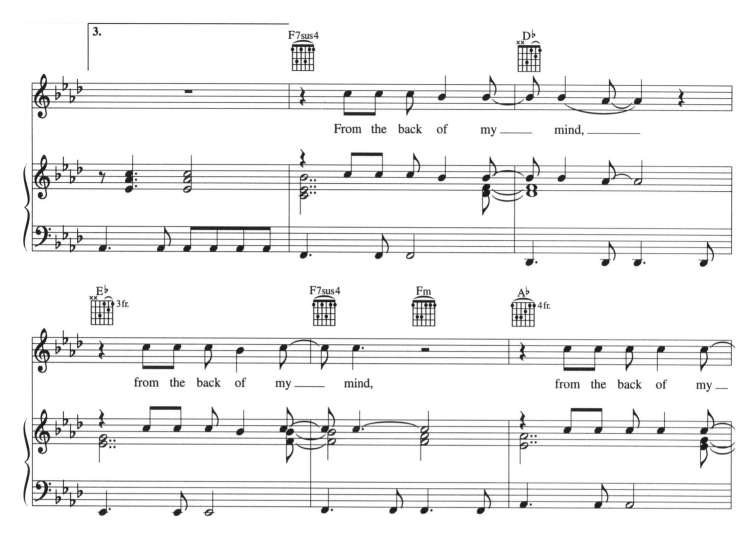

**3.**

F7sus4           Db

From the back of my _____ mind, _____

E♭      F7sus4    Fm     A♭

from the back of my _____ mind,      from the back of my _____

E♭      B♭       F

*D.%.al Coda*

_____ mind,     from the back of my _____ mind. _____

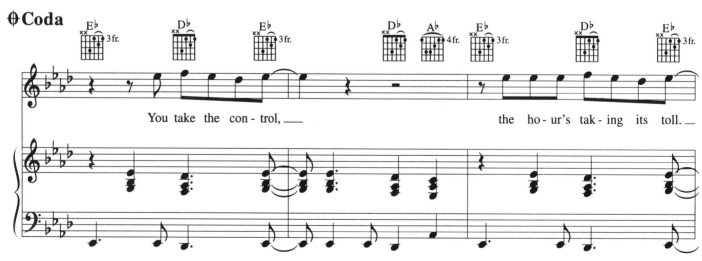

**✪ Coda**

E♭    D♭    E♭       D♭   A♭   E♭     D♭     E♭

You take the con - trol, _____          the ho - ur's tak - ing its toll. _____

Verse 2:
Everything that you need is right beside you
But you turn it away.
You've got an instinct inside that's there to guide you
When you make your own way
We chase the future today.

Verse 4:
Everything that you see stands right before you
If you open your eyes.
Understand your beliefs and we'll expect you
To know where it's at,
Man it's as simple as that.

# WALKAWAY

Words & Music by John Power

♩ = 84

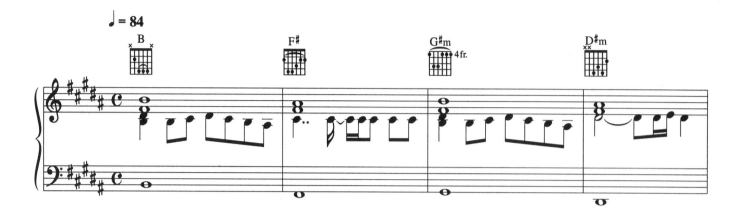

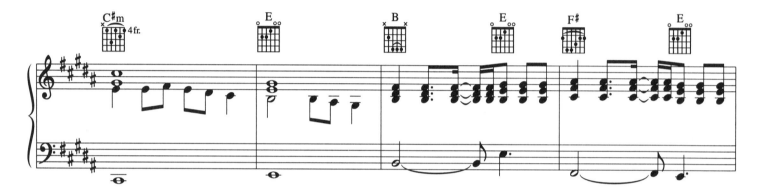

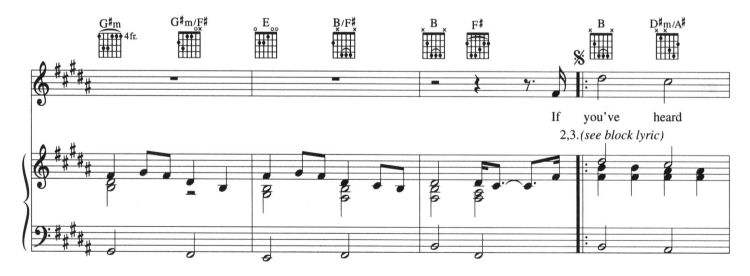

If you've heard

2,3.(see block lyric)

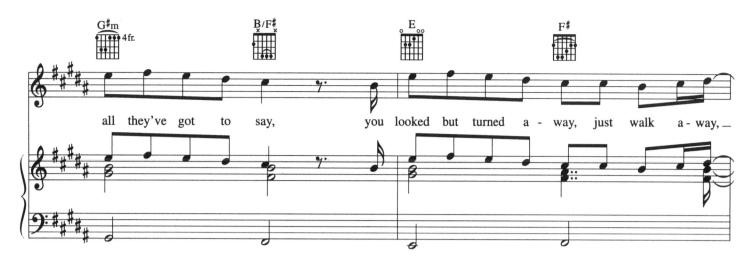

all they've got to say, you looked but turned a - way, just walk a - way, __

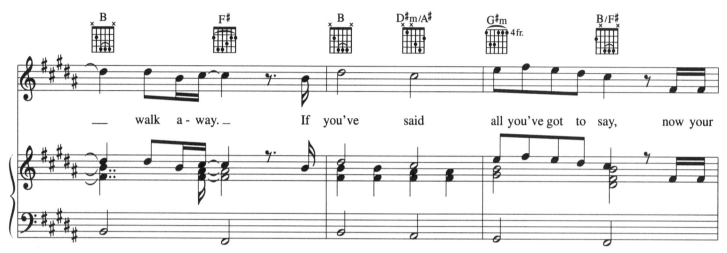

__ walk a - way. __ If you've said all you've got to say, now your

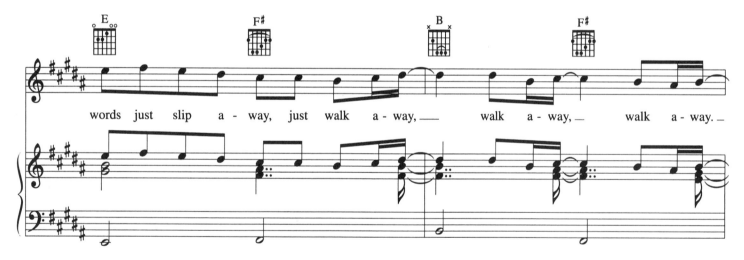

words just slip a - way, just walk a - way, __ walk a - way, __ walk a - way. __

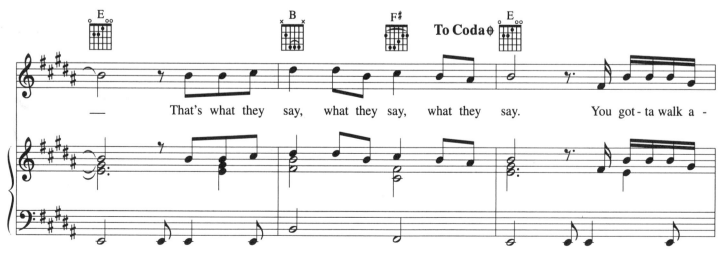

__ That's what they say, what they say, what they say. You got - ta walk a -

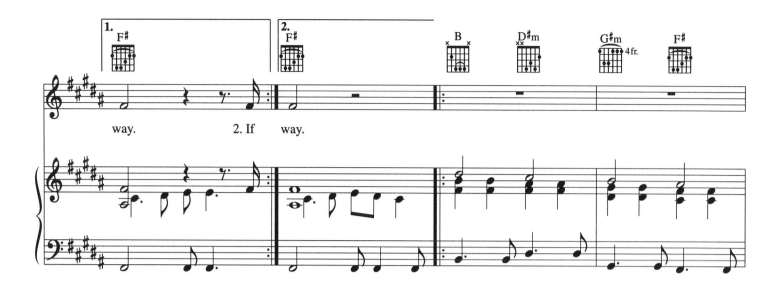

way.          2. If    way.

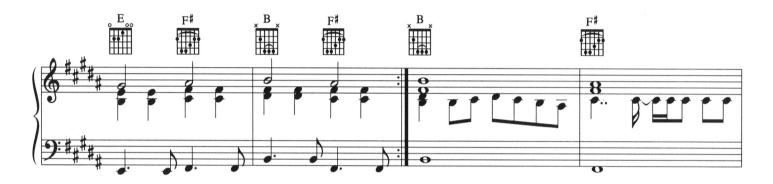

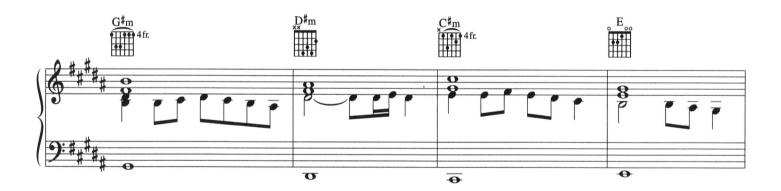

Now you must be-lieve __ me,     you nev - er lose your

*Verse 2:*
If you've played all the games they play
You played them yesterday, just walk away, walk away.
If you've been where they wanna go
Seen all they've got to show just walk away, walk away, walk away.
That's what they say, what they say, what they say,
Gotta walk away.

*Verse 3:*
If you've proved all there is to prove
Got nothing left to lose, just walk away, walk away.
If you've done all there is to do
Ain't nothing left for you, just walk away, walk away, walk away.
That's what they say, what they say, what they say,
Walk away... *(to Coda)*

# REFLECTIONS

Words & Music by John Power

-ing ___ the two. ___ It's dream re - al - i - ty,

try - ing to break ___ free ___ and wake ___ me, dream re - al - i -

ty, ___ try - ing to break free ___ from this world, ___ from the

world. _____ 2. Well I can ___

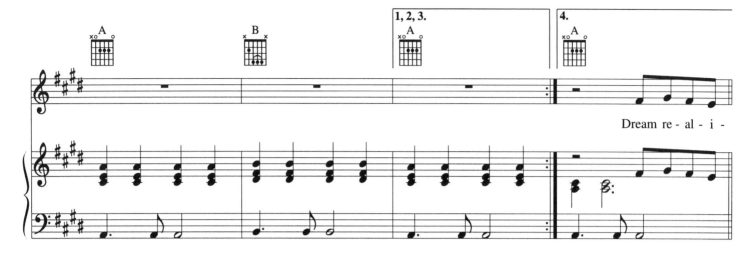

Dream re - al - i -

ty, try-ing to break __ free and wake __ me, dream re - al - i -

ty, try-ing to break free from this world. __

Free from this world, __ set me free from this world, __

**Verse 2:**
Well I can feel your reactions
Reacting with mine.
And now I sense things are happening
And they're happening on time.

**Verse 3:**
Well I can feel your direction
Directing me on line
And I believe you're responding
Responding to your mind.

# TWO OF A KIND

Words & Music by John Power

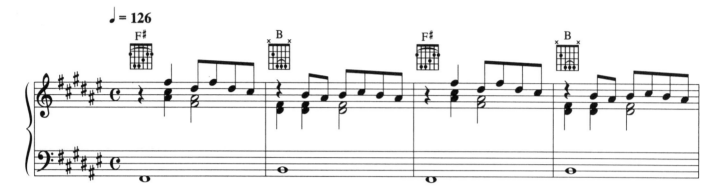

1. Can you help me, help me if ___ you can, ___ for I'm in
2,3. *(see block lyric)*

need of a help - ing hand, ___ or some ___ un - der-

stand - - - ing. I feel I'm sink-ing,

sink-ing with the boat, I'm try-ing to stay a-float,

some-one throw me some hope.

Can you help me to set my course, I'm aim-ing for

bet - ter shores ___ and when I get there, I ___ hope to find

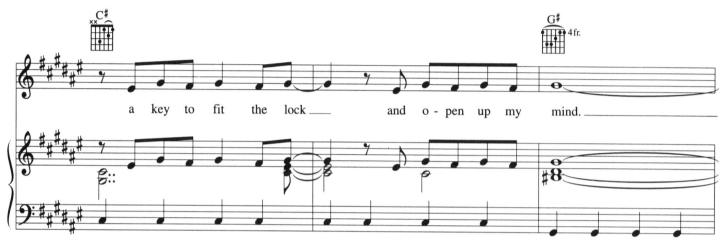

a key to fit the lock ___ and o - pen up my mind. ___

___ Please throw me a ___ line,

I'm lost here in ___ time, I'm locked in my

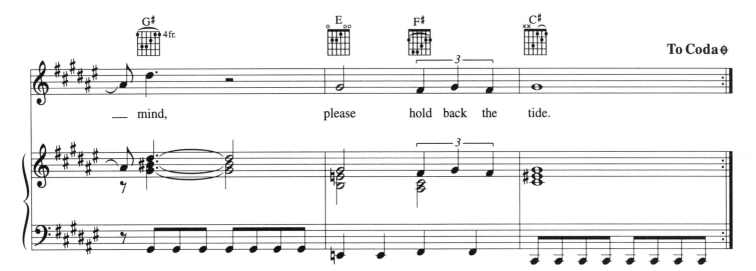

— mind,                    please        hold   back   the            tide.

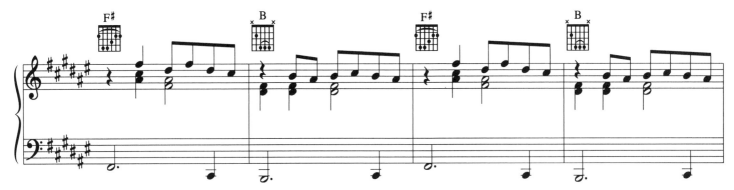

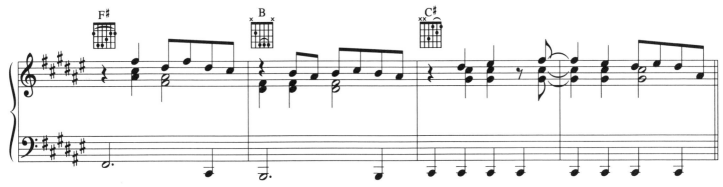

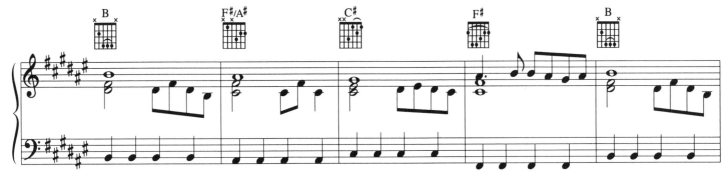

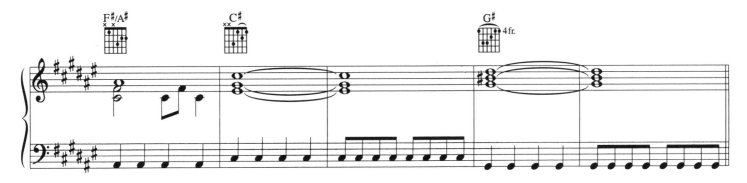

Life push-es hard ___ when you're down ___

and we're all lost ___ un-til we're found, ___

un-til we're found, ___ un-til we're found. ___

Please throw me a ___

*Verse 2:*
Feel I'm drifting,
Drifting with the tide
Let the ocean be my guide,
Waves I shall ride.
And then I'm sinking.
Sinking in the depth
And I'm trying to catch my breath,
But no breath is left.

Can you help me to set my course
I'm aiming for better shores
And when I get there I hope to find
A key to fit the lock and open up my mind.

Please throw me a line
I'm lost here in time
I'm locked in my mind
Please hold back the tide.

*Verse 3:*
And from nowhere
Someone shines a light
And sends to me some sight
And gives back some life.
And she gave
All that she can give
She gives me the will to live
Love's eternal gift.

So at last we meet again
Together now until the end
We are as one and all is saved
And now it's time to turn, turn the final page

Together we find
A place here in time
Together in mind
All ways to shine.

# HISTORY

Words & Music by John Power

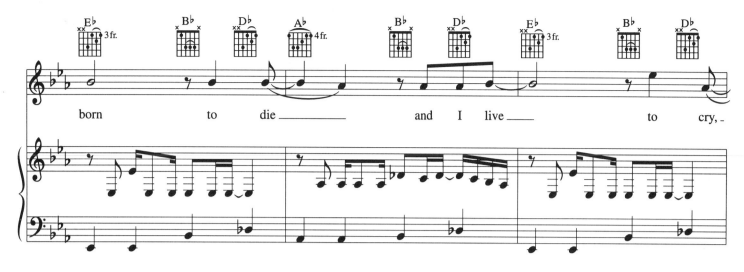

born to die _____ and I live _____ to cry, _

_____ and I'm your tor - men - ted soul, black-ness _ that holds to all _

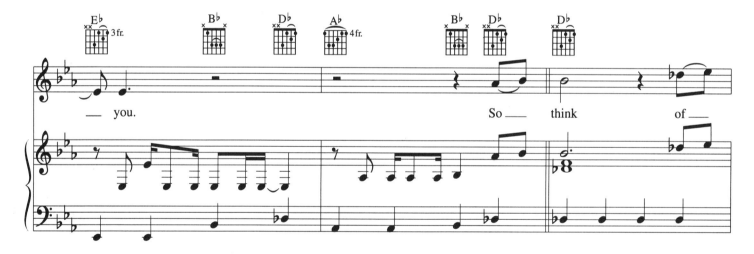

_ you. So ___ think of ___

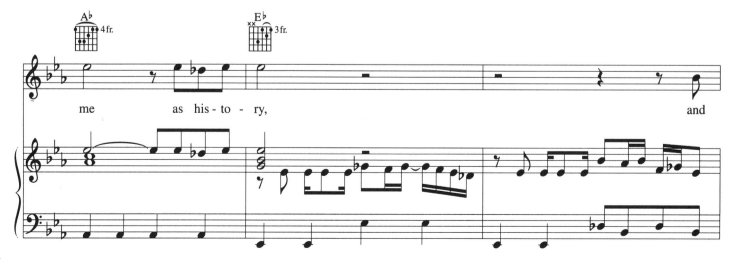

me as his - to - ry, and

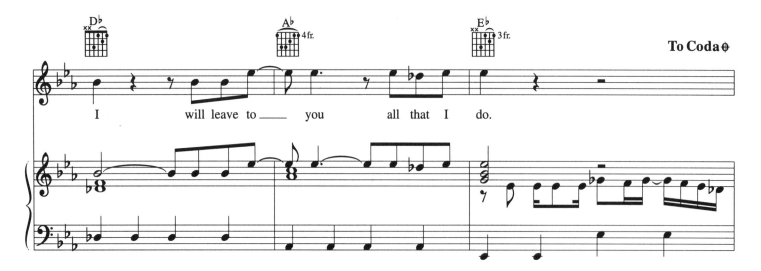

I will leave to ____ you all that I do.

**1.** **2.**

2. Well I've

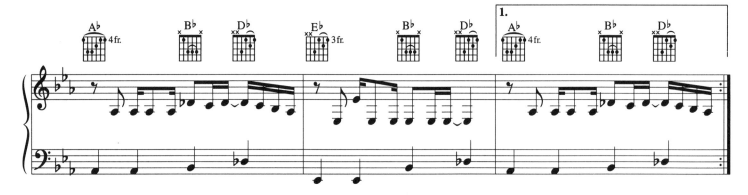

**1.**

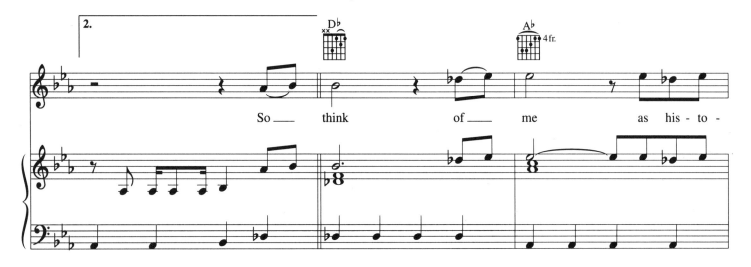

**2.**

So ____ think of ____ me as his-to-

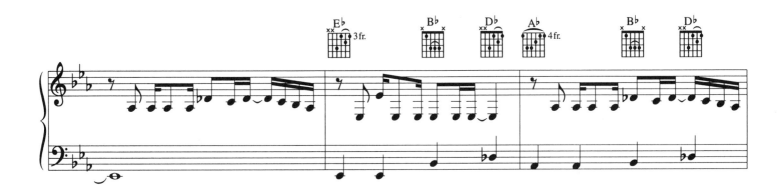

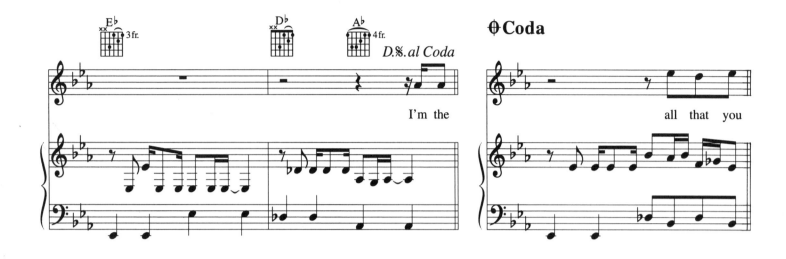

**⊕ Coda**

Printed and bound in Great Britain by
Caligraving Limited Thetford Norfolk

*Verse 2:*
Well I walked this earth
Since woman gave birth
I'm a seed that's sown
The harvest is grown in all you.
But I've laid to waste
My future in haste,
I'm the crops that have failed,
The burden that's nailed to all you.

*Verse 3:*
I'm the cloud that bursts
I rain down for your thirst
I'm the thunder you hear
The lightning that spears your night.
I'm the shadow that is cast
I project all your past
I'm the children you burn
The cross that is turned by all you.

11/96 (26398)